Disney's
Year
Book
1984

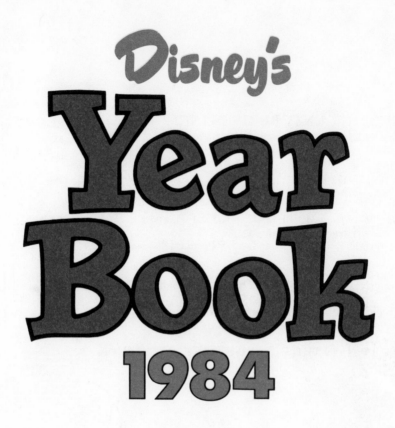

Disney's Year Book 1984

GROLIER ENTERPRISES INC.
Danbury, Connecticut

GROLIER ENTERPRISES INC.
Robert B. Clarke   *Publisher*

ISBN: 0-7172-8136-1
ISSN: 0273-1274

Illustration Credits and Acknowledgments

6-11–© Walt Disney Productions; 24-26–Randa Bishop; 28–© Flip
and Debra Schulke/Black Star; 29–NASA; 30–© Walt Disney
Productions; 32–Koala Technologies Corporation; 33–Nelson Max,
Lawrence Livermore National Laboratory; 34–Sirius; 35–Computer
image by: Rob Cook, Loren Carpenter, Tom Porter, Bill Reeves,
David Salesin and Alvy Ray Smith. © Lucasfilm Ltd. (LFL) 1983. All
rights reserved; 48-50–Courtesy of Scholastic Photography
Awards, conducted by Scholastic Magazines, Inc. and sponsored by
Eastman Kodak Company; 51–© Wolfgang Bayer/Bruce Coleman,
Inc.; 53–J. Spurr/Bruce Coleman Inc.; 54–Russ Kinne/Photo
Researchers; 55–© R. C. Hermes/Photo Researchers; 56-59–Jenny
Tesar; 72–Jet Propulsion Laboratory; 74–NASA; 75–Jet Propulsion
Laboratory; 76–© United States Postal Service; 77-78–Courtesy
Knapp Communications; 79–© United States Postal Service;
80-83–©Kjell B. Sandved/Smithsonian Institution, Washington, D.C.

Contents

Epcot Center:
Welcome to a Magic Journey   6

It's Hard to Go Straight
When You're Crooked   12

Summer Training for
Junior Astronauts   24

Computers Can Outdraw Anyone   30

Twiddler's Thumbs   36

Moments in Time   48

Strong-Armed Starfish and
Other Amazing Animal Tales   51

Sticker Stationery   56

Tennis Menace   60

Sailing to the Stars   72

Olympics, U.S.A.!   76

Seeing with Animal Eyes   80

Ferdinand Finds a Friend   84

EPCOT Center

WELCOME TO A MAGIC JOURNEY

The newest addition to Walt Disney World in Florida is Epcot Center, a magical learning and entertainment experience for children and parents alike.

Stretching across 260 acres, with the towering sphere of Spaceship Earth as its symbol, Epcot Center is like a huge and permanent World's Fair, connected to the Magic Kingdom by a monorail that also circles the Center.

Visitors ride up into the dome of Spaceship Earth (left) to watch the story of communications unfold. Vehicles of the future are on display at the World of Motion (below).

At The Land exhibit, an enormous greenhouse shows how foods will grow in the future. The Kitchen Kabaret show (above) features singing and dancing by models of various foods.

Epcot Center opened in 1982 and has already had millions of visitors to its two main areas, Future World and the World Showcase. In Future World, children and parents take an exciting journey through time and space. On this journey, they go from the distant past when dinosaurs walked the earth, through today's fascinating period of new technology and change, to an amazing future world of computerized living—not just on earth but in space and under the sea.

There are seven major exhibition pavilions in Future World—on energy, communications, computers, transportation, imagination and creativity, agriculture, and the lifestyles of the 21st century.

Across a lagoon from Future World is the World Showcase. Here there are nine pavilions, each devoted to a different country and built in a familiar architectural style of the country: the United States, Mexico, Canada, the United Kingdom, Germany, Italy, France, Japan, and China. Each of the pavilions presents a panorama of the history, crafts, entertainment, and, at numerous restaurants, the foods of the country.

At the Universe of Energy, models of huge dinosaurs dramatize the creation of oil, coal, and other fossil fuels.

The Horizons exhibit (above) makes the 21st century come alive as it shows how science and technology will change people's lives.

Epcot Center itself is a marvel of the latest technology. Visitors go through the Future World exhibits riding in computer-controlled vehicles. And the exhibits feature lifelike figures, called Audio-Animatronic, that move and talk in an amazingly realistic way at the command of computers.

As marvelous as Epcot Center is, the Walt Disney technicians and artists who created it are already working on ways to make it even more exciting. In the years ahead, they will be creating new exhibitions and pavilions for Future World and the World Showcase—to insure that Epcot lives up to the name Walt Disney himself gave it: *E*xperimental *P*rototype *C*ommunity of *T*omorrow.

The Journey into Imagination exhibit (below) explores the world of creativity. Visitors can test their own creative talents in the electronic playground called the Image Works.

IT'S HARD TO GO STRAIGHT
WHEN YOU'RE CROOKED!

Mickey opened *The London Times*.
"Sleuth! Look at THIS!" he exclaimed.

Sleuth read the bold, black letters:
PROFESSOR NEFARIOUS RETIRES
FROM CRIME!

"Well, I'll be!" he exclaimed, missing his
crumpet and spreading jam on his sleeve.

Mickey began to read aloud. "Professor
Nefarious, England's Greatest Crook, today

announced his retirement from crime. The Professor stated that criminal activities had become too tiring. 'From now on,' the Professor said, 'I am just a law-abiding citizen.' Police and civil officials called the Professor's retirement a real service to the community."

Mickey stopped reading. "I don't believe it," he said.

"But Mickey," Sleuth answered, "if you read it in *The Times*, it must be true!"

At that moment, across town, merry laughter was ringing through the halls of the College of Criminal Knowledge.

"HAW! HAW!" laughed Armadillo,

holding *The Times* in his fat little hands. "Get this, Perfesser! *The Times* says you're retiring."

"What dope told 'em a dumb story like that?" asked Sidney.

"Yeah, dope!" said Fliplip.

Professor Nefarious stood up. "*I* am the dope who told them that dumb story."

The merry laughter ceased.

"YOU, Boss?" Sidney gulped.

"But, Boss, we're no good without YOU!" Fliplip whined.

"So what?" the Professor growled. "You're no good *with* me, either!"

Suddenly, the Professor smiled. "Relax! That story is just the first step to my finest hour as England's Greatest Crook!"

The Professor then held up a stack of white envelopes. "This," he said, "is step two."

He handed them to Fliplip. "Mail these," he said to the short crook in the long scarf.

The next morning, the postman delivered
a large white envelope to Sleuth's house.

"We've been invited to the Professor's
retirement party!" Mickey said.

"Oh, goody!" Sleuth exclaimed.

"I still think he's up to something,"
Mickey said.

"Oh, Mickey! Don't be a party-pooper!"

When Sleuth and Mickey arrived that
evening, the Professor's party was in full
swing. The College of Criminal Knowledge
was full of famous guests.

"Jolly decent of the professor to retire
from crime," the president of the London
Bank was saying to the president of the
London Steamship Company. The president
of the London Diamond Company and the
president of the London Mink Coat
Company agreed.

Suddenly Professor Nefarious climbed up
on his desk. "Time for the scavenger hunt!"
he announced.

The Professor handed out slips of paper.
"Bring back what it says on your paper,"
the Professor explained. "We will decide the
winner when everyone has returned."

"What does our slip say?" Mickey asked
Sleuth as they went out the door.

"The Crown Jewels of England."

"WHAT!" Mickey gasped.

"That should be easy," Sleuth went on.
"I'm sure the Queen will lend me her
jewels."

"Wait a minute, Sleuth! There's . . ."

"Mickey, if you spoil this scavenger hunt,
I shall never forgive you!" Sleuth said.

Two hours later, the Professor's guests began to return. The president of the London Bank brought a million pounds in small bills. The president of the London Mink Coat Company returned with sixteen mink coats. The president of the London Diamond Company brought back a shopping bag full of diamonds. And the president of the London Steamship Company returned with four first-class tickets to

Zanzibar on a boat leaving at midnight.

"Stay here, gentlemen. We will be right back to announce the winner," the Professor said, gathering up the money, the minks, the diamonds and the tickets. Nefarious,

Sidney, Armadillo, and Fliplip disappeared into the back room and out the back door.

"Put that stuff in the car and let's get out

of here!" the Professor ordered.

"But, Boss, Sleuth hasn't come back yet with the Crown Jewels!" Armadillo said. "Don't we want to . . ."

"No time for that!" Nefarious snapped. "We must get away before my guests find out they've been tricked!"

"Where to, Boss?" Sidney inquired.

"Pier thirteen of the London Steamship Line. And then . . . Zanzibar!" Nefarious chuckled, pointing to the four tickets in Fliplip's hand.

At that very moment, Sleuth and Mickey were talking to the Queen's butler.

"If you want to see the Queen, you'll have to go to Zanzibar. That's where she is," the butler said.

"Come along, Mickey!" said Sleuth. "We're going to Zanzibar! There's a boat leaving tonight, and we're going to be on it!"

It took the long-legged detective only a few minutes to run to the docks. He turned and looked for Mickey, but the little fellow had not yet arrived.

Just then, guess who drove up!

"Stop here!" Professor Nefarious shouted.

"Ah!" thought Sleuth as he saw the four figures get out of the car. Perhaps these fellows are also going to Zanzibar tonight."

He approached the four figures. "Beg pardon, chaps . . ."

"Sleuth!" the four crooks exclaimed.

"Grab him!" the Professor yelled.

They pounced on Sleuth and tied him up.

"Why, Professor Nefarious," said Sleuth. "Fancy meeting you here. Is this part of the scavenger hunt?"

"No," Nefarious answered. "It's part of the crime of the century!"

"Then you aren't going to retire?"

"No. I'm going to take a vacation."

Suddenly Mickey appeared, followed by three policemen. "Oh, no, you don't!" said Mickey.

Zanzibar Docks ➡

"Mickey!" cried Sleuth. "What are you doing here?"

"I went back to the Professor's place after you left," Mickey said, untying Sleuth. "I found out what his game was."

The Great Detective and his pal watched the policemen handcuff the three criminals.

Three criminals?

"Wait a minute!" Mickey said. "Where's Nefarious?"

Fliplip pointed to the steamship. "He jumped on board when the cops showed up," Fliplip said. "Poor Professor Nefarious!"

"What do you mean, 'poor'?" complained Sidney. "He got away, didn't he?"

"Not really—he *stowed* away. I've still got the tickets. The Professor will be peeling potatoes all the way to Zanzibar!"

Summer Training For Junior Astronauts

Can sixth-grade students learn to be astronauts in one week? They can try—at a very special camp in Huntsville, Alabama, called the United States Space Camp.

Campers learn how rockets are built and then tour Rocket Park, which contains many rockets from the U.S. space program.

The camp is run by the Alabama Space and Rocket Center, the world's biggest space museum, with the help of NASA. Girls and boys from all over the United States—and other countries, too—attend the camp. To apply, the campers must have finished sixth, seventh, or eighth grade and

In the Lunar Odyssey (above), campers feel their weight triple during a mock moon launch.

must have a recommendation from a science teacher. In 1983, the campers paid $350 for the week, which covered their accommodations, meals, and teaching materials.

During their busy week, the campers use actual NASA equipment as they learn about rockets, space flight, and what it takes to be

an astronaut. They discover how rockets
are designed, how they work, and how they
fly. They make and launch model rockets.
And they study the future of space flight.

As they go through their astronaut
training, the campers try out the space suits
and helmets used by America's astronauts.
They learn about the food that astronauts
eat on a flight and about the life-support
systems that make space flight possible.

They learn about weightlessness, too.
First they weigh themselves on a special
scale that shows them what they would
weigh on the moon—one sixth of their
weight on earth. Then they enter the "moon
walk trainer" where they actually feel

weightless and can leap and jump as if they were really on the moon.

The campers also practice splashdown landings in a swimming pool, using rubber life rafts and a recovery cage just like the ones used in an actual space capsule landing.

The high point comes on the last day when the campers take part in a make-believe shuttle flight. All the campers are

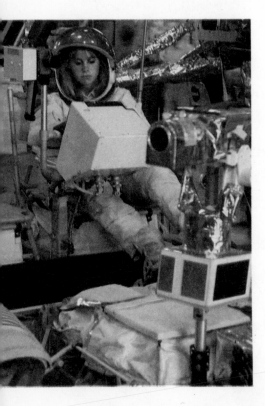

In an Apollo Lunar Rover (left), a camper wears an astronaut's space suit. Campers also learn how it feels to be weightless, like astronaut Thomas Mattingly during a space shuttle flight (right).

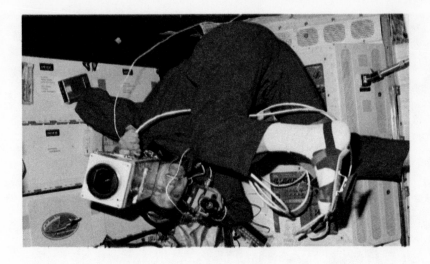

assigned to shuttle crews. Some work in
mission control. Others work in the
spacecraft cockpit. The crews go through all
the steps of a real shuttle mission: checkout,
countdown, launch, orbit, and return to
earth. It's an exciting experience, and it lets
the campers put to use all they've learned
during the week.

The final event is a lunch. The campers
eat astronauts' freeze-dried foods. After
lunch, each camper is awarded Space Camp
wings. They're not real astronauts yet. But
maybe someday they will be, and they'll
ride out into space just like today's
astronauts do.

COMPUTERS
Can Outdraw Anyone

As if computers weren't amazing enough,
they are now being used to create art.
Computers haven't yet replaced paper,
pencils, brushes, and paints—or the artists
who use them. But they are being used to
produce amazing works of art called

The Walt Disney movie Tron *(left) combined people with computer art to show the hero battling villains inside a computer.*

computer graphics.

The first computer graphics were used in the 1960s to train military pilots. These pictures showed pilots what it was like to fly a plane.

Computer graphics became much more popular in the 1970s. Industries began to use computer graphics to make designs for many things, from nuclear missiles and video games to advertisements for jeans.

Scientists began to use computer graphics to make pictures of things too small for the human eye to see. On a computer screen, a scientist could construct a model of a tiny molecule and then color all its parts. Then the scientist could turn the image to view it from each side.

Computer graphics are what make video games as exciting as they are. Many home computers now let you make your own computer graphic designs. You can then use

these designs in games that you create.

Computers are also being used to create animation and special effects for movies. The first film to use computer graphics in a big way was the Walt Disney movie *Tron*. Fifteen minutes of the action, including people and vehicles, were created by computers.

Artists are now producing art on their computer screens, and some museums have

One way to create computer art is with a drawing tablet (left). Computer art helps scientists to visualize very complicated molecules, such as the DNA molecule (below).

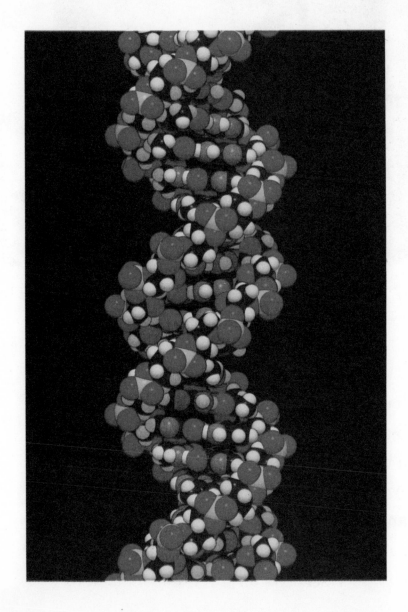

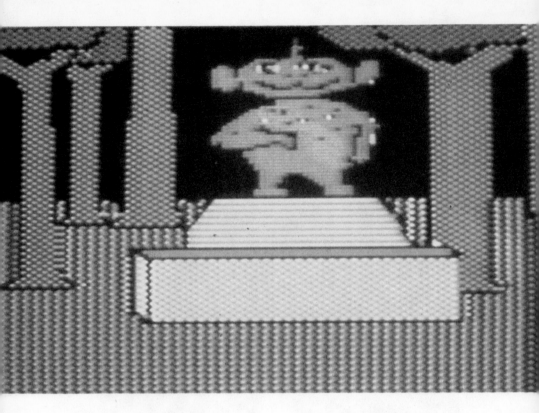

Home computers now have programs that let you create your own video games (above).

had exhibits of this art. Computers can be a big help to an artist. A computer can create a three-dimensional picture of an object. And it can produce a view of the object from any angle.

Then, while the artist watches, the computer can turn the object around or

On advanced computers, artists can make very detailed and realistic pictures like this one.

inside out or make it pass right through another object.

And with a computer, an artist never has to erase a drawing or start over with a fresh sheet of paper. To change anything or to put a color in, the artist just presses a button—and the computer does the rest!

TWIDDLER'S THUMBS

Once upon a time, a woodcarver lay awake, thinking about all the work he had to do.

"Soon I will finish that doll for Lisa," he thought. "And there's the chest for the cobbler, and the wagon for the doctor, and the quilt rack for Aunt Sarah. Ahh, I have so much work!" And with thoughts of work buzzing in his head, he finally fell asleep.

When the woodcarver awoke, he was still thinking about work. He was about to fix himself some eggs and heat up a muffin, when he heard a KNOCK! KNOCK!

"More work," the woodcarver muttered. When he opened the door, a note fluttered to the ground. He picked it up and read: "Dear Woodcarver: I must have that bookcase this afternoon. Your friend, A. J. Lardo."

"Friend?" sputtered the woodcarver. "He doesn't even give me time to eat breakfast!"

The woodcarver grabbed his coat, slammed his door, and marched off to town. He went straight to the tent of a traveling magician.

"Hello," called the woodcarver. "Anybody in there?" A cloud of smoke poofed up.

"Can't a body eat breakfast in this town?" said the smoke.

"I want to talk to the magician," said the woodcarver, peering around. "Where is he, anyway?"

"Here I am!" Suddenly the smoke turned into the magician himself. "Now—you wanted to talk to me?" he said.

The woodcarver explained. "I'm a woodcarver—a good one, you see—and I never have time for anything but carving wood. I'm *tired* of it!"

"My, my, you do have a problem," said the magician. "What do you want me to do?"

"Well," the woodcarver said, "I can't seem to say no to anyone. But if you were to fix my hands so I couldn't carve . . ."

"Done," said the magician. "From this day forward, whenever you try to work, you will only be able to twiddle."

"Twiddle?" asked the woodcarver.

"Twiddle," said the magician. "Now go home and eat your breakfast and let me finish mine. When you try to carve you will

simply twiddle your thumbs."

When he got home, the woodcarver walked to his workroom and reached for his tools.

Sure enough, as the magician had
promised, the woodcarver's thumbs were
twiddling madly, around and around and
around.

"Ha, ha!" he shouted, dancing about the
room. "It *is* true: I can't carve!"

He danced out the door and went to the
first house up the lane.

"Aunt Sarah," he called, "come to the
door!"

"What is it, Woodcarver? Are you all
right?" asked Aunt Sarah.

"I'm fine, Aunt Sarah. I've never been better. But I can't carve your quilt rack. I'm twiddling, you see." He held up his hands, which really were busy twiddling.

Aunt Sarah said, "Why yes, I do see. Well, as long as you're twiddling, come sit for a while and have some tea and cookies."

After a while, the woodcarver left and went to the doctor's house. When he told his twiddling tale, the doctor said, "I

understand perfectly. Now, come in and have some tea and cookies and a little chat with me."

At the end of the day, with his tummy full of tea and

cookies, the woodcarver lay in bed,
thinking. "This has been the best day I've
had in years. I don't even miss my work."

So day after day, the woodcarver
twiddled and walked, sipped tea and talked.

One morning he walked through the
forest. There he came upon a wonderful
piece of wood.

"What a beauty this is," he exclaimed. "It

would be a shame if this wood goes to
waste. Someone should make something
from it, and I'm the only one who can."

He held the wood in his hand. He almost wanted to throw it away and pretend he'd never found it. "I guess I'll *have* to carve it," he finally said with a heavy sigh. "I'll go home right now and get it over with."

So the woodcarver carried the piece of wood home. He walked into his old workroom, but when he tried to pick up his chisel, he found himself twiddling!

"Oh, no!" he cried. "I don't think I *can* stop twiddling! Now that I *have* to carve, I can't! What a mess I'm in!"

Hoping that his friends could help him, the woodcarver called them all together and explained his problem.

"We'll help," they all said. The blacksmith suggested some iron gloves. The woodcarver pulled them on and reached for his chisel. Before anyone could blink, his hands had clapped together, and the iron thumbs began clanking around one another.

"Wait!" said Aunt Sarah. "Maybe the spell only works on your tools. Try mine."

But before the woodcarver could even touch Aunt Sarah's whittling knife, his

hands flew back together and twiddled fast and furious.

Suddenly, the doctor pushed his way through the crowd. "I have it!" he cried. "Here is the cure—my special anti-twiddling tonic."

The woodcarver drank the tonic down.

"Now pick up your chisel. Your thumbs won't twiddle," said the doctor.

Everyone watched the woodcarver's hand as it neared the chisel. First it twitched. Then it turned. Finally, it thumbed its way back to meet his other hand and the two thumbs twiddled like long-lost friends.

"That's that," said the woodcarver. "My only hope is to find that magician."

So the woodcarver went home and packed his bag. He put in the chunk of wood, just in case he got cured.

He had gone only a short distance when he came upon a young girl. She was crying.

"There, there, little girl. Why must you cry so hard?" he asked.

The poor child couldn't even talk. But she held up her doll and the woodcarver could see that it was split right down the middle.

The woodcarver didn't even think. He sat
right down and took out the chunk of wood.
Soon he had carved the most beautiful doll
he'd ever made.

Then he looked around. "Little girl!
Where are you?"

There was a soft POOF! and sitting
where the girl had been was the magician.

"Where is that poor little girl?" asked the
puzzled woodcarver.

"There was no little girl," the magician said, smiling. "There was only myself. I believe you were looking for me . . ."

"Yes, I was," answered the woodcarver. "I want you to lift that twiddling spell."

"What twiddling spell?" asked the magician.

The woodcarver looked down at the beautiful doll he had carved. Then he looked up at the magician, and they both laughed.

That day the woodcarver went home a far wiser man. He sat the doll up on the shelf in his workroom to remind himself: Work is done best when you *want* to do it, not because you *have* to do it.

Hot Air Balloon *by Paul Herbert, Reseda, California.*

MOMENTS IN TIME

A good photographer stops a moment in time and turns it into a picture. The talented young photographers who took

Pilings *by David Gibbons, Wellesley, Massachusetts.*
Lac Leman *by Mikeljon Nikolich, Unionville, Pennsylvania.*

these pictures captured light and shadow, color and excitement on film so that others could share their vision—of a young boy's daydream, the angles of a bridge, the windy motion of a giant balloon, the sharp beauty of swans in the water.

Andrew Dreaming *by Augie Bevill, Magnolia, Texas.*

The photographs on these pages were among the winners in the 1983 Scholastic/Kodak Photo Award Program. This program is open to students in junior and senior high schools in the United States and Canada. The winners receive scholarships and other awards.

Strong-Armed Starfish
and Other Amazing Animal Tales
Crocodile Cradles

A crocodile's jaws are strong enough to crush the bones of a large deer. But crocodiles can also use their jaws in a very gentle way.

When a baby crocodile is ready to be

born, the mother helps it to come out of its shell by gently cracking the shell with her jaws. The mother then picks up the baby in her mouth and carries it gently to the water.

As the baby grows, the mother will carry it from place to place in her jaws.

Flying Feet

Ostriches can't fly, but they can run very fast. Ostriches can run at a speed of 35 miles per hour for as long as half an hour. For shorter periods of time, they can run at a speed of 43.5 miles an hour. This is faster than a greyhound or a racehorse.

Strong-Armed Starfish

Starfish usually eat mussels, clams, and oysters. These shellfish can close their shells very tightly, but the starfish is very good at opening them.

The starfish has hundreds of suction cups on the bottom of each of its five arms. The starfish opens the shells by clamping its five arms over the shellfish and using the suction cups to pull open the two halves of the shell.

The starfish then pushes its stomach through the narrow opening between the shells. The stomach digests the clam, oyster, or mussel inside its own shell.

Educated Eaters

The koala of Australia is a very picky eater. It generally eats only the leaves of the eucalyptus tree. But it is so finicky about its food that it only eats some leaves from some eucalyptus trees.

Zoos with koalas have a great deal of trouble feeding them. In fact, the only two zoos in the United States that have been able to keep koalas are the San Diego Zoo and the San Francisco Zoo. At these zoos, there are eucalyptus trees growing nearby.

Camouflaged Crabs

The sponge crab is a decorator crab. Decorator crabs are crabs that are very good at disguising themselves with things they find in the ocean, like shells and seaweed.

The sponge crab disguises itself with a piece of sponge. It uses its front claws to cut out this piece of sponge from a live sponge. The piece the crab cuts is exactly the size of its back. The crab holds the sponge in place over its body with its back legs, which it uses only for that purpose.

When an octopus comes along, the crab pulls in its head. Then it looks like a sponge, which the octopus does not like to eat.

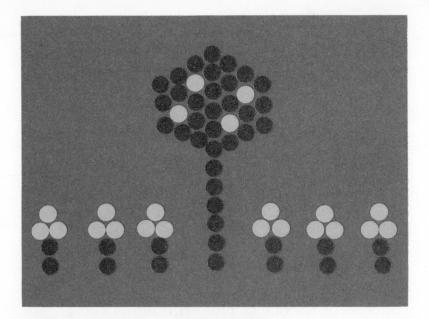

STICKER STATIONERY

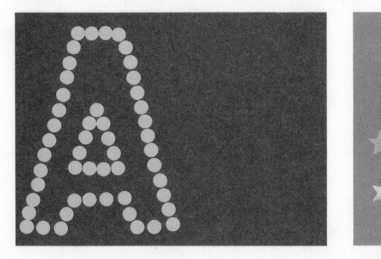

Stickers are fun to collect and fun to use. They come in many different colors and shapes. One nice thing you can do with stickers is to make your own stationery. You can use the stickers to spell your name or initials, to make a flower, tree or animal, or to create a special design of your own.

WHAT YOU'LL NEED

Stars, dots, hearts, or any other kind of stickers. Paper. Pencil. Pen.

WHAT TO DO

To make note-size stationery, fold a sheet of paper in half. Put your design on the outside. Write your note inside.

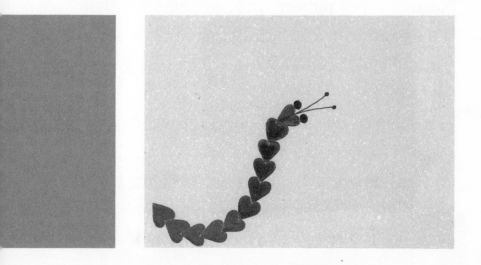

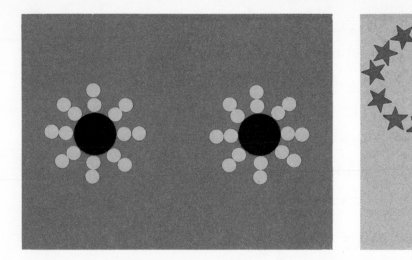

To make letter-size stationery, don't fold the paper. You can put the design at the top or the bottom or make a border around the entire sheet. Just remember to leave enough room for what you want to write.

The first step is to draw the design on a piece of scrap paper. After you've sketched the design, draw it lightly in pencil on the stationery. Then follow the design as you paste on the stickers.

It's fun to use lots of different colored stickers. And after you've pasted the stickers down, you can draw on them. Use a pen to give a worm its eyes and antenna. Or draw a bee sitting on your sticker flower.

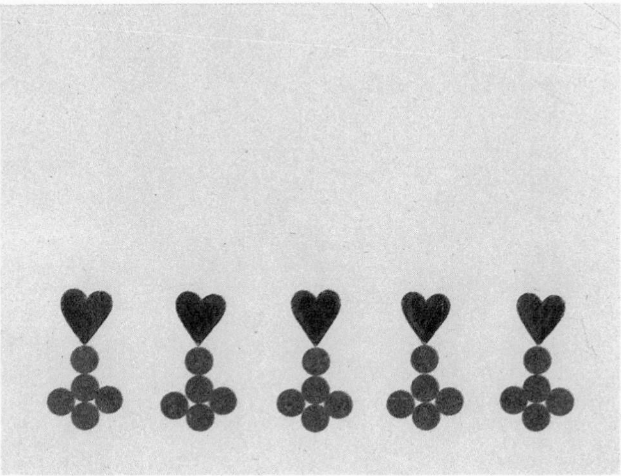

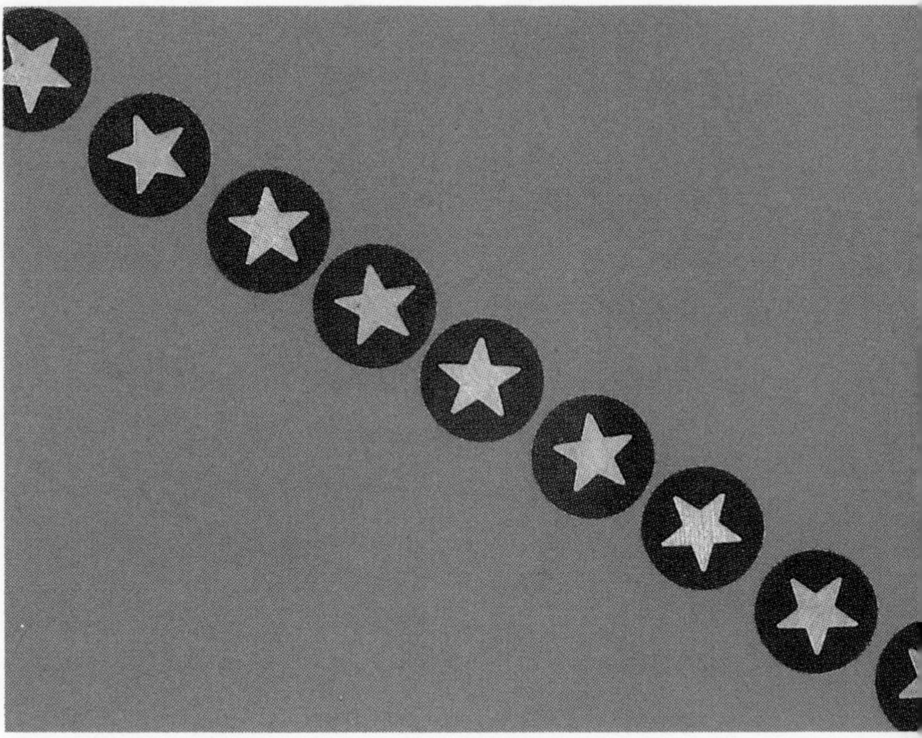

TENNIS MENACE

"Hey! Wait for me!" shouted Sport Goofy, running for the bus at the airport. The bus lurched to a stop.

"Gawrsh, thanks," Sport Goofy said.

"That's okay," the driver answered. "Somebody else is late, too." He pointed to another person who was running toward them.

The bus full of young people was on its way to the National Junior Tennis

Championships. Sport Goofy was one of the sponsors. About halfway down the aisle he spotted an empty seat. Then he recognized Allen and Beth sitting behind the empty seat. He knew both of them. "Hi!" he said. "Nice to see you both made it to the finals again!"

"Hi, Sport Goofy! We hoped you'd see us," said Allen.

"How could I miss you?" answered Sport Goofy. "Why don't I sit here, and we . . ."

But Sport Goofy found that the seat had already been taken.

"Go find your own place," a voice sneered.

"Gawrsh, sorry," said Sport Goofy. "That seat *was* empty."

"Well, it isn't now."

Sport Goofy quickly found another seat. "Who's that guy?" he whispered.

"They call him 'Slammer,' " Allen answered in a low voice. "He's made quite a name for himself this year."

"They say he's got a serve that no one can return," said Beth.

"Shucks, Allen," said Sport Goofy. "Don't worry about him. Just play your best. That's what will make you a real winner."

But Allen wasn't convinced. "That's easy for you to say, but I'm probably going to have to play him—if I make it that far. I don't know why I even bothered to show up."

Sport Goofy gave

Allen a pat on the shoulder. "Think about Slammer later," he said. "Here we are at the tournament center."

The next few days were full of activity. Each morning and afternoon Allen and Beth met Sport Goofy on the court for practice. Allen kept making mistakes. Sport Goofy knew it wasn't like him. He knew Allen was worried about the Slammer. But he hoped the boy would snap out of the slump on his own.

The morning before the tournament, Allen played very badly. He and Beth were hitting the ball back and forth. But poor

Beth was chasing the ball too often. Allen couldn't seem to get his serves within bounds.

Sport Goofy interrupted their play. "I think we all need a change of pace," he said.

"Oh, Sport Goofy," sighed Allen, "I can't do anything right."

"You're trying too hard to be like the Slammer," Sport Goofy pointed out. "It's too late to change your game. Just do your best."

"He's right, Allen," Beth said. "Come on, why don't we all go bike riding?"

"Great idea," agreed Sport Goofy.

That afternoon, Sport Goofy played two
exhibition sets with the local tennis star,
Molly Volley. Allen and Beth went along.

When Sport Goofy walked onto the court,
he dropped his racket. "Oops!" he said.
Then he pulled a big bandage from his
pocket and stuck it on the racket.
Everybody laughed.

Sport Goofy served first. He took three
tennis balls in his left hand, threw them all
up in the air, and hit one. Goofy's serve
went *zing!*—into the net.

"Try one ball at a time," someone called.
Again everybody laughed.

"Hee-yuk!" laughed Sport Goofy. "I guess it's time to play tennis." This time his serve was good. Molly returned it easily. They hit the ball back and forth for a few minutes. Then Sport Goofy missed.

But he and Molly were evenly matched. They each won one set. Then they shook hands.

"Great playing, Molly," said Sport Goofy.

"You're no slouch yourself," answered Molly. "Thanks for a good match."

The next morning Sport Goofy found Allen looking even gloomier.

"What's the matter?" asked Sport Goofy.

"It's the Slammer," said Allen. "I know he'll beat me."

"Allen," said Sport Goofy, "if you think that way, the Slammer won't beat you. You'll beat yourself."

"But his serve . . ." said the boy.

"A serve isn't all there is to a game," Sport Goofy said sternly. "Stop thinking about the Slammer and start thinking about your own game. We're all rooting for you."

Allen walked onto the court, thinking hard. Sport Goofy was right—what mattered most was doing his best.

The Slammer strutted onto the court, making mean remarks about Allen to the crowd. Allen tried not to listen.

The Slammer served first. He walked
back to the baseline and stood there to
make Allen nervous. He flipped the ball up
and down. Then suddenly he threw the ball
up and brought the racket down with a hard
thwack! Allen jumped, but the ball slammed
into the net.

"Just wanted to see if you were on your
toes," the Slammer called with a sneer. He
tossed the ball up for his second serve and
then caught it. He watched Allen to see if
he would jump. But this time Allen was

steady. The Slammer frowned. Then he finally served, sending the ball sizzling over the net. This was the impossible serve that had made him the talk of Junior Tennis. He was sure it would win him the tournament.

But a change had come over Allen. He had shut the Slammer out of his mind, and now he could concentrate on his game. The serve was hot, but Allen was ready for it. He sent it back over the net with a full, easy swing.

Allen's return caught the Slammer by surprise. *Slam!* went his racket. *Whiz!* went the ball—right into the net.

After that, it seemed that the "slam" had gone out of the Slammer.

When Allen won, the crowd cheered. The Slammer threw his racket on the court and stomped over to the net. He shook Allen's hand, but he didn't say a word.

Sport Goofy congratulated Allen. "I hate to say 'I told you so,' " he chuckled, "but—I told you so, didn't I?"

"You can say it all you want, Sport Goofy," laughed Allen. "Next time, I'll listen."

"You do that," said Sport Goofy. "Let's see how Beth did in her match."

Beth had also won her first match.

"Gee," said Beth, looking at the lineup for the next day's play. "Tomorrow I play Rosie. Her backhand is a killer."

"Whoa," said Sport Goofy, "Don't *you* start worrying. Just remember . . ."

"Let me, Sport Goofy," laughed Allen. " 'Play your best. That's what will make you a real winner!' "

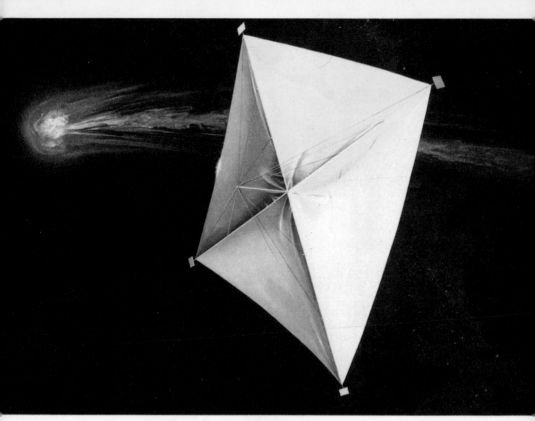

Sailing
to the Stars

Someday, giant ships may sail out into
the farthest reaches of space. They will be
equipped with solar sails that capture the
power of the sun. Just as the sails on
sailboats use the force of wind to move the

boat, these solar sails will use the force of light.

Sunlight is a form of radiation. It travels out from the sun in little packets far too small for the eye to see. These moving packets are a source of energy. In space, where everything is weightless, the force of these packets would be strong enough to propel a solar sail.

Scientists in the United States and other countries are now working on detailed plans and models for the first space sailing ships. They would have huge solar sails—perhaps several miles across. The larger the sail, the more light it would capture and the faster it would go.

Close to the earth, the space sailing ships would travel slowly. But farther out in space, they would begin to pick up speed. Solar sails might travel nearly as fast as rocket-powered space ships, at speeds of

124,000 miles (200,000 kilometers) an hour.
And they would have a great advantage
over rocket-powered spaceships. Their
power supply—sunlight—would be free and
unlimited.

Space sailing ships could cruise the solar
system on exploratory voyages. They could
sail past the moon and head out to distant
planets on a leisurely trip. They might even
be used in an interplanetary shuttle.

*Many satellites now orbiting in space, such as
this mapping satellite, have solar sails.*

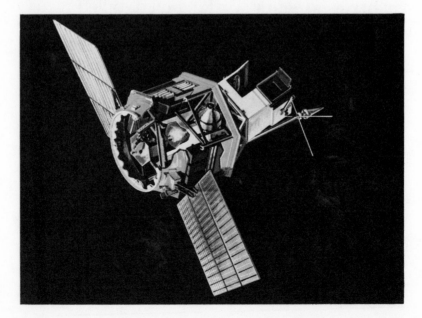

The Heliogyro solar sail has twelve sails that are like the blades of a helicopter rotor.

Rocket-powered ships would transfer their passengers and cargo to and from the surface of a planet.

On some night far in the future, astronomers may see a new constellation in the sky—a fleet of space sailing ships cruising among the stars.

Olympics 84
USA
13c

OLYMPICS, U.S.A.!

In 1984, for the first time since 1932, the Summer Olympic Games will be held in the United States in the city of Los Angeles.

Olympic athletes train long and hard for the honor of competing in the Olympics. If they win a medal, they know they are the best in the world in their sport.

Throughout history, since the first Olympiad was held in Greece in 776 B.C., artists have pictured the skill and glory of

Colorful U.S. stamp shows racing yachts under sail (left). A runner's legs seem to leap out of the sky on an Olympic poster (right).

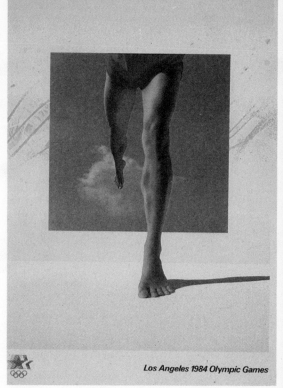

Los Angeles 1984 Olympic Games

Olympic athletes in action. For the XXIII Olympiad in 1984, Olympic athletes and the spirit of Olympic competition will be honored in posters and stamps.

At the invitation of the Los Angeles Olympic Organizing Committee, sixteen posters have been done by some of the world's most noted artists, including the English artist David Hockney and the American artist Robert Rauschenberg.

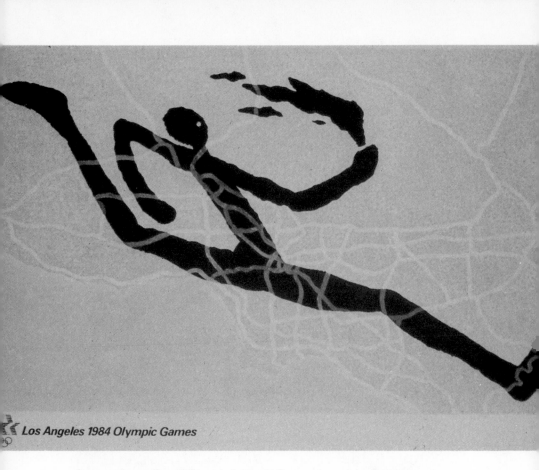

*Carrying the Olympic torch, a runner leaps
across a map of Los Angeles in this dramatic
poster (above). Many of this year's Olympic
stamps show women athletes in action (right).*

The stamps are the largest collection of
Olympic stamps ever issued by the United
States Postal Service. There are 24
individual stamps, three postal cards, and
one overseas aerogramme. The stamps
show more than 24 different sports,

including gymnastics, swimming, soccer, skiing, speedskating, cycling, hockey, and wrestling. Nine of the stamps feature women's events.

The stamps have been designed and painted by Robert Peak, a noted American illustrator. He specializes in portraying figures in action in brilliant colors. His stamps are an exciting tribute to the Olympic theme: "Higher, Faster, Stronger."

Stamps will be issued by the United States Postal Service in 1983 and 1984. The Postal Service is also offering a free Olympic Stamp Collector's Kit. Write United States Postal Service, Olympic Stamp Program, Philatelic Sales Division, Washington, DC 20265-9985.

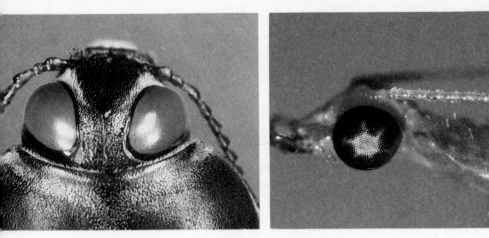

Seeing
With Animal Eyes

Animals see with their eyes very much like humans see with theirs. Like the eyes of humans, the eyes of animals can sense light. Nerves carry the message of light to the brain. The brain then creates a picture or image of what the animal or human is looking at.

But animals' eyes are also different from human eyes in many ways. Camels and elephants, for example, have eyes that are on the side of the head. Most animals that

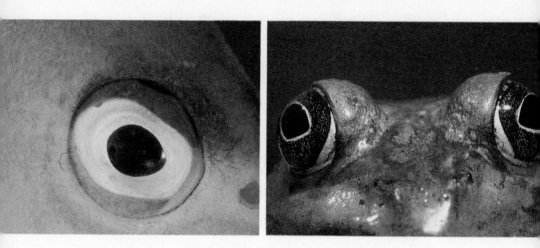

Animals' eyes may differ greatly in appearance. Shown from left to right are the eyes of the Goliath beetle, the golden-eyed lacewing, the queen angelfish, and the frog.

eat plants have eyes like this. These animals see a different picture or image with each eye. They can also see things far to the side. This helps them to see animals trying to sneak up on them and attack them.

Animals that hunt and eat other animals are called predatory animals. Their eyes are at the front of the head, and they see the same image with each eye. Because their eyes are in front, they can look forward and tell how far away the animal they are hunting is.

Most birds have eyes on the side of the head. But predatory birds like hawks have eyes in front. All birds have a third eyelid which is transparent and moves from side to side. When the bird moves this eyelid, it keeps its eyes moist. Fish have no eyelids at all. The water they swim in keeps their eyes wet.

A frog has eyes that are like the periscope of a submarine. The frog's eyes pop up from its head. When the frog is partly under water and can hardly be seen, its eyes are above the water and it can look around.

Insects probably have the most unusual

eyes of all animals. Almost all insects have two large eyes on the side of the head. These eyes are called compound eyes. They are made up of many tiny lenses. Each tiny lens sees just a small part of what the insect is looking at. The parts each lens sees are then put together like a jigsaw puzzle in the insect's brain to make a complete picture.

Many insects also have three other eyes between their compound eyes. These simple eyes can only see light, not images.

Shown from left to right are the eyes of the camel, the Victoria crowned pigeon, the elephant and the robber fly. The elephant and the camel have long lashes to keep dust and dirt away.

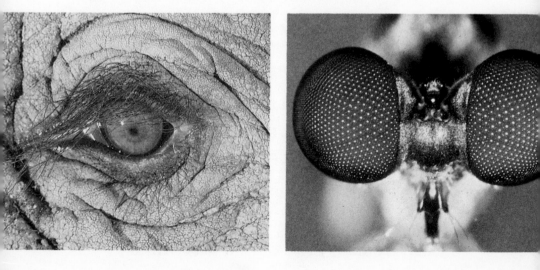

Ferdinand
Finds a Friend

One sunny spring day when he awoke
from his nap, Ferdinand the bull went to
look for some flowers to smell. Off he
strolled down the dusty, dappled lane.

Before long, Ferdinand came to a new
house. It had been built by the Widow
Garcia, a small, gray-haired lady. Like

Ferdinand, she loved flowers, and in front
of her new house she had planted a beautiful
rose garden.

The Widow was out shopping when
Ferdinand strolled by. He immediately
noticed her roses. He sniffed at one bush.
He sniffed at a second. He sniffed at three
bushes in the back row. Never had
Ferdinand smelled such a beautiful
perfume! He lay down among the bushes,
ever so carefully. And he sniffed, and he
sniffed, and he sniffed!

When Ferdinand saw the Widow coming

down the lane, he
stood up and greeted
her with a great, big
"Mooooo!"

The Widow
shrieked. Ferdinand
was a big, fierce-
looking bull, and she
naturally thought he
was about to ruin
her roses. So she ran into her yard, grabbed
a rake and chased poor Ferdinand away.

Then she threw down her rake and
marched off to talk to his owner. When she
arrived at his hacienda, she banged on the
front door.

"See here, mister rancher," she began. "I
can't have that bull in my flowers. You're
letting a dangerous animal run loose," she
said. "I've never heard of such a thing!
Bulls should be kept behind strong fences!"

The Widow stomped her foot. "You must
lock him up," she demanded, "or I shall
complain to the mayor!" Then she turned on

her heel and stalked away.

The rancher sighed. "I suppose she is right," he said to his children. "Bulls do belong behind fences, even gentle ones like Ferdinand. Go bring him back to the corral. We'll have to keep him there."

Their hearts were heavy and their steps were dragging, but the children obeyed their father. They brought Ferdinand back to the stout corral. They tried very hard to make him happy. They fed him fistfuls of green grass, handfuls of oats, shiny red apples, and yummy yellow pears. But day by day he got thinner and thinner, sadder and sadder.

"We must do something," said the rancher's oldest daughter.

"You're right," agreed her brother. "Perhaps if we take him for walks, his appetite will come back."

Their father gave them permission, but
warned them to hang on tightly when they
passed the Widow Garcia's house. So they
began to take Ferdinand for daily walks.

One day, as the children and Ferdinand

passed her house, the Widow looked up
from her garden. "It really is too bad," she
said to herself. "I can see that the poor bull
is unhappy. But he can't be let loose in my
roses again."

She turned away to scatter some plant
food around a pink rose. Then she heard an
odd rumbling sound. "If I didn't know

better," she mused, "I would think that
was . . ."

She looked up as the noise grew louder.
". . . HOOFBEATS!" she exclaimed. "Oh,
my heavens!" Out on the meadow she saw a
rambunctious bunch of young bulls. They
were bawling and bashing and bellowing
and butting. And they were headed straight
for her house!

"My roses!" she squealed. "What can I
do? I can bully one bull, but not six."

Since she couldn't think of anything else
to do, the Widow ran toward the bulls.
"STOP!" she shouted, as loud as she could.

That surprised the six boisterous bulls.

No one had ever shouted at them before.
They skidded to a stop and stood watching
her.

The bulls looked at the Widow. The
Widow looked at the bulls. "Now what do I
do?" she asked herself. When she got no
answer, she took her red apron in both
hands and flapped it at the bulls to shoo
them away.

Now, an apron flapping looks a lot like a
bullfighter's cape flapping, don't you agree?
At least that's what the bulls thought. They
pawed the ground with their big hooves.

They snorted through their fierce noses.
They lowered their heavy heads and waved
their wicked-looking horns. And they
charged!

The bulls chased the Widow and her
flapping red apron all over the meadow.
Finally she reached her house and slammed
the front door in their faces.

By this time, Ferdinand and the rancher's
two children were passing by on the way
home from their walk. And by this time, the
bulls had discovered the roses. As the
horrified Widow watched from her window,

they stomped into her garden and munched on her flowers.

This was too much for Ferdinand. How dare those fellows mistreat those flowers? Toss went his head. *Snort!* went his nose. Down went his very sharp horns, and off he charged, straight at the Widow's tormenters.

Of course, even brawny young bulls were no match for Ferdinand. His temper was up. In no time at all he had sent them off home, tails tucked tamely between their legs.

The Widow came out of her house.

"I saw it all from my window," she said. She went up to Ferdinand and took his face between her hands. "How wrong I was about this fellow! He chased those naughty young bulls away and rescued my roses. Your Ferdinand is a hero!"

Suddenly they heard a shout from the meadow. It was the rancher and his oldest son. They had followed the young bulls.

"Mrs. Garcia," began the rancher, "my

bulls have eaten your roses. How can I apologize?"

"Now, now, my good man," she replied, "it's not as bad as that. They didn't really do too much damage."

"You are very understanding, Ma'am," frowned the rancher. "But today I have learned something. You were right: Bulls belong behind strong fences."

"No," objected the Widow, "I was only partly right. *Most* bulls belong behind fences, but not this one. Ferdinand is welcome to visit my garden any time."

So once more Ferdinand was allowed to run free in his field. He could doze and dream under his favorite cork tree. And once in a while, as a special treat, he would walk down the dusty, dappled lane to visit his new friend, the Widow Garcia, and her wonderful garden of roses.

YOUR
WEIGHT
ON THE
MOON